Published by Hinkler Books Pty Ltd
45–55 Fairchild Street
Heatherton Victoria 3202 Australia
www.hinkler.com.au

hinkler

© Hinkler Books Pty Ltd 2008, 2011

Illustrators: Melissa Webb, Anton Petrov, Omar Aranda,
Suzie Byrne, Mirela Tufan and Dean Jones
Prepress: Graphic Print Group
Typesetting: Graphicraft Limited

Images © Shutterstock.com: Seamless wallpaper pattern © Ozerina Anna;
Oval gold picture frame © Nodff.

ISBN: 978 1 7418 5018 5

Printed and bound in China

Contents

Puss in Boots

Once upon a time, there was an old miller who died, leaving nothing for his three sons apart from his mill, his donkey and his cat.

The three sons decided to split this poor property between themselves. The eldest son took the mill, the second son took the donkey and the youngest son received nothing but the cat.

Understandably, the youngest son was quite disappointed that his share was so poor. 'My brothers may make a handsome enough living if they combine their shares together,' said the youngest son, 'but, for my part, once I have eaten this cat and made a hat of his skin, I must die of hunger.'

The cat heard the youngest son saying all this, but he appeared to take no notice of it. Instead, he turned to his master with a grave and serious air and said, 'Do not worry yourself so, my master. All you have to do is give me a bag and get a pair of boots made for me so I may scamper easily through the thorns and brambles, and you shall soon see that, as my owner, you don't have such a poor share after all.'

Although the youngest son did not entirely trust what the cat had said, he remembered that he'd seen the cat play cunning tricks to catch rats and mice. The cat had hung himself by the heels to make the mice think he was dead and had hidden himself in the corn, so the cat's master did not completely despair of the cat helping him out of his situation.

Once his young master had given him his new boots and bag, the cat was very pleased. He thought he looked very gallant and elegant in his shiny boots. Wearing his new boots, the cat hung his bag around his neck and held its strings in his two forepaws. He went out into the fields and found some tender, juicy grass to put in the bag.

Then the cat went to a nearby rabbit warren where he knew a great number of rabbits lived. He stretched himself out on the ground as though he were dead, making sure that some of the grass in the bag was poking out. The cat lay there, waiting for some young rabbits, not yet acquainted with the tricks of the world, to come along and be tempted by the food in his bag.

The cat had barely lain himself down when a young and foolish rabbit hopped up. It sniffed at him, and then climbed into the bag to eat the tender grass. At once, the cat drew closed the strings, catching the rabbit unawares.

Proud of his catch, the cat headed off to the palace and asked to see the king. He was shown to the king's court, where he made a low bow to those assembled there.

'I have brought you, Sire, a rabbit from the warren of my noble lord and master, the Marquis of Carabas (which was the title that the cat was pleased to invent for his master),' said the cat. 'He commanded me to bring this to Your Majesty as a gift.'

The king was very pleased with the gift, as he was extremely fond of tasty rabbit.

'Tell thy master,' said the king, 'that I thank him and that I am well pleased with his gift.'

The cat departed, happy with the outcome of his endeavour.

Shortly after this, the cat hid himself amongst some tall corn in a field, again with his bag around his neck. He stood as still as a statue near the tastiest looking corn he could find and held his bag open. It wasn't long before two partridges came along and, in their efforts to eat the corn, fell into the open bag. At once, the cat drew the strings closed, catching both birds.

As he had done with the rabbit, the cat went to the palace and made a present of the partridges to the king. In the same way, the king received the partridges with great pleasure. The king even commanded his servants to reward the cat with a gold coin.

Over the course of the next two or three months, the cat continued to take some of his master's game as a gift to the king. The king was always very pleased to receive these offerings and he rewarded the cat with a gold coin.

One day, the cat discovered that the king was to go for a drive along the riverside to get some fresh air and enjoy the sunshine. The cat also discovered that the king was taking his daughter, the most beautiful princess in the world, with him on the drive.

The cat went to his master and said, 'If you will follow my advice, your fortune is made. You don't have to do anything apart from going to the river and having a bath at the spot that I show you. Just leave all the rest to me.'

The cat's master was confused as to why the cat was asking him to do this, but he did as the cat advised. While he was bathing, the king's carriage passed by.

At once, the cat cried out at the top of his voice, 'Help! Help! My master, the Marquis of Carabas, is drowning! Help! Help!'

Hearing the noise, the king looked out of the carriage window. Seeing the cat who had brought him so many gifts of game, he commanded his guards to immediately run to the assistance of his Lordship, the Marquis of Carabas.

As the king's guards were pulling the marquis out of the river, the cat hid his master's clothes under a large, heavy rock. Then the cat went up the coach and told the king that while his master was bathing, some thieves had come and stolen his clothes, even though the cat had cried out, 'Thieves! Thieves!' as loudly as he could. At once, the king commanded some guards to run and fetch one of his best suits for the Marquis of Carabas to wear.

The king was exceedingly polite to the marquis once he had put on the fine suit, as the clothes set off his good looks (for he was very handsome) and the king saw that his lovely daughter was very taken with the marquis. The marquis had only to exchange two or three respectful and tender glances with her before they found themselves in love. The king invited the marquis to join them on their drive.

The cat was overjoyed to see his plan succeeding. He marched on ahead of the coach and met some people mowing in a meadow, which was owned by a cruel ogre.

'Good mowers,' said the cat, 'the ogre who owns this field has asked me to tell you that if you do not tell the king that the meadow you are mowing belongs to the Marquis of Carabas, he will chop you up into tiny pieces and cook you in his pot!'

The mowers were very frightened of the ogre, so when the king drove past and asked them who owned the meadow, they all immediately answered, 'The Marquis of Carabas does, Your Majesty.'

'You have a fine meadow there,' the king said to the marquis.

'Yes Sire,' replied the marquis, thinking quickly. 'It gives me a good harvest every year.'

The cat continued on ahead, until he met with some reapers, who were harvesting corn in another field owned by the ogre.

'Good reapers,' said the cat, 'the ogre who owns this field has asked me to tell you that if you do not tell the king that this corn belongs to the Marquis of Carabas, he will chop you up into tiny pieces and cook you in his pot!'

And when the king passed the field in his carriage and asked them who owned it, they all replied, 'The Marquis of Carabas owns this corn, Your Majesty.'

The cat went on ahead again and told everyone he met that the ogre said to tell the King that the land was owned by the Marquis of Carabas. Everyone was so scared of the ogre that they did.

Eventually the cat came to the ogre's home, which was an enormous, stately castle. The ogre was the richest ogre ever known. The cat, who had discovered the ogre's magical talent, asked to see him, saying he couldn't pass by without paying his respects. After some grumbling, the ogre let him in and made him sit down.

'I have been told that you have an amazing gift,' said the cat to the ogre. 'They tell me that you can change yourself into any creature you choose, such as a lion. Surely this is not true?'

'It is true! If you don't believe me, let me prove it to you,' said the proud ogre, and he turned himself into a fierce, snarling lion.

The cat seemed so terrified at the sight of the lion that he jumped up and tried to climb on to a cupboard, which was rather awkward because of his boots. When he saw the ogre had finally returned to his normal form, he slowly climbed down.

'That is impressive!' said the cat. 'But I have also been told that you can take on the shape of the smallest animal, such as a mouse. Surely, though, that is impossible.'

'Impossible?' roared the ogre. 'Watch and you shall see!'

And the ogre changed himself into a tiny mouse and began to run around the room. The cat immediately sprung on him and ate him up!

Just then, the king's coach drove by the fine castle. The king, wanting to see who lived there, ordered the coach to go in. The cat, hearing the coach coming over the drawbridge, came out to meet them and said to the king, 'Welcome to the castle of my Lord, the Marquis of Carabas!'

'What? My Lord Carabas!' cried the king. 'Does this fine castle belong to you too? Let us see inside, if you please.'

The marquis helped the princess down from the coach and they followed the king inside the castle. There was a magnificent feast prepared in the Great Hall for the ogre. The king was perfectly charmed with the fine qualities of the marquis, as was the princess, who had fallen completely in love with him.

The king could see that his daughter was in love with the marquis and he was so impressed on seeing the vast estates and fine castle that the marquis owned that he insisted that the marquis and the princess get married that very day.

They lived happily ever after, and the cat became a great lord. He never had to chase mice again, although he sometimes did for fun!

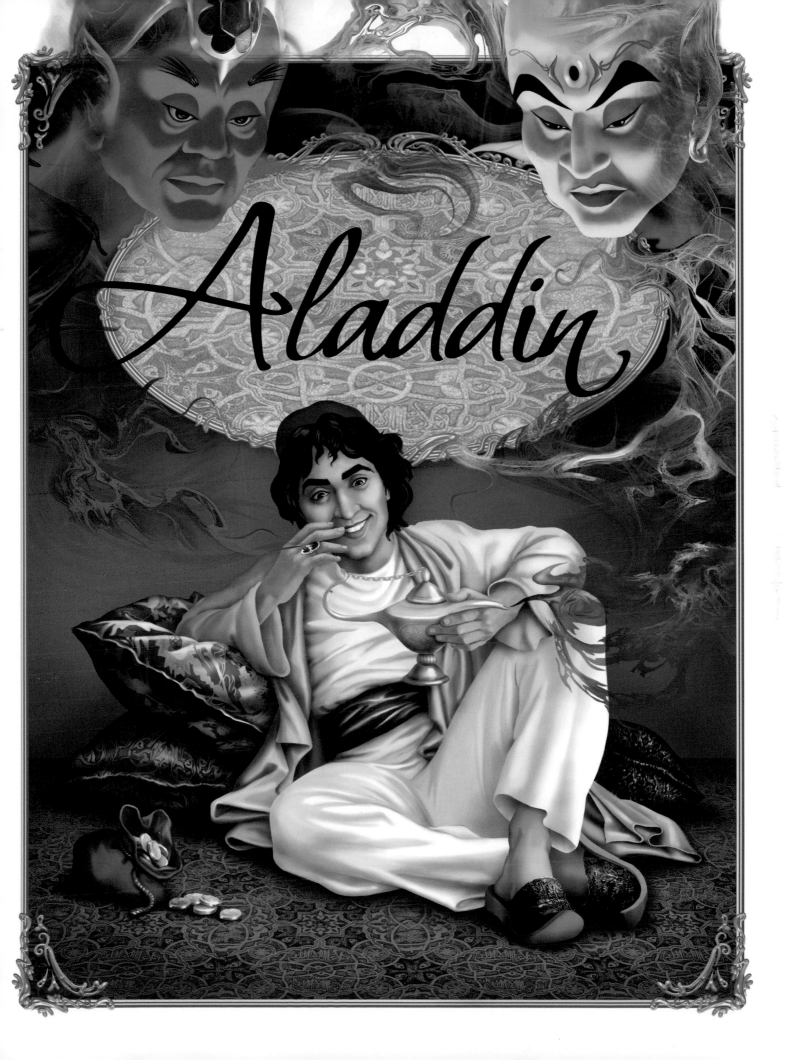

Aladdin

Once there lived a young man named Aladdin. His father, a tailor, had died of grief because his son was so lazy and idle. Despite this, Aladdin did not mend his ways.

One day, Aladdin was approached by a stranger, who asked him his age and if he was the son of Mustafa, the tailor. 'I am, sir,' said Aladdin, 'but my father died some years ago.'

'I thought you looked like him!' exclaimed the stranger, who was a magician. 'I am your father's brother! Tell your mother I will come and visit.'

Aladdin ran home and told his mother about his new-found uncle. 'Your father had a brother,' she said, 'but we thought he died.'

However, she prepared a meal and welcomed the magician when he arrived. 'Don't be surprised that you don't know me,' said the magician. 'I have been out of the country for forty years.'

When his uncle heard that Aladdin had no profession, he offered to stock a shop for him to make his mother proud. The next day, the magician took Aladdin out to buy some new clothes. His mother was overjoyed when she saw her son looking so fine.

The following day, the magician took Aladdin out of the city. They journeyed for a long while until they reached the mountains. At last, they came to a narrow valley. 'We will go no further,' said the magician. 'Gather some sticks and I shall make a fire.'

When it was lit, the magician threw a powder on the fire and said some magic words. The ground shook and a stone slab with a brass ring was revealed. Aladdin tried to run away in fear but the magician stopped him. 'Don't be afraid,' said the magician. 'Beneath this stone lies a treasure. It shall be yours if you do exactly as I say.'

When he heard this, Aladdin forgot his fears. Following the instructions of the magician, he grasped the brass ring and pulled, saying the names of his father and grandfather. The stone came up easily and revealed a set of steps leading down.

'Go down,' said the magician to Aladdin. 'You will find a corridor leading to three large halls. Tuck in your gown and go through them. Do not touch the walls or you will instantly die. The halls lead to a garden of fruit trees. Go through the garden until you reach a stone terrace where a lighted lamp stands. Pour out the oil in the lamp and bring it back to me.'

The magician took off a ring and gave it to Aladdin. Aladdin followed his uncle's instructions. He picked up the lamp and walked back through the garden, taking some fruit off the trees as he went. Aladdin got back to the mouth of the cave and the magician cried out, 'Be quick and give me the lamp!'

But Aladdin refused, as he wasn't safely out of the cave yet. The magician flew into a terrible rage. He threw more powder on the fire and said some magic words. The stone rolled back into place, trapping Aladdin in the cave.

The magician fled far away to another country. He was not Aladdin's uncle, but an evil magician who had read of the lamp in his books. He knew it must be retrieved by the hand of another. The magician had picked Aladdin for this very reason and planned to kill him after he got the lamp.

For two days, Aladdin remained in the dark, crying. Realising he was stuck, he clasped his hands in prayer. As he did so, Aladdin rubbed the ring, which the magician had forgotten to take from him. Suddenly, an enormous genie rose up, saying, 'I am the slave of the ring! What is your wish?'

'Save me from here!' answered Aladdin. The stone rolled back and Aladdin climbed out and struggled home.

Aladdin told his mother about the magician's trickery. He showed her the lamp and the fruits, which were actually precious stones. His mother went to cook, but she had no food or money, so Aladdin said he would sell the lamp. It was very dirty, so he rubbed it with his sleeve to clean it. Instantly, a huge genie appeared. It bowed and asked, 'What will you have?'

'Fetch us something to eat!' said Aladdin. The genie conjured up a feast on silver bowls and cups. Aladdin told his mother about the cave, the ring and the lamp. At first she begged him to sell them, but Aladdin convinced her they should use them.

After they had eaten, they sold the silverware. Aladdin and his mother were able to live like this for several years. They ate the food provided by the genie, sold the silverware and lived off the money until they needed more.

One day, the sultan ordered everyone to stay inside and close their shutters. The princess was going to the bathhouse and no one was permitted to see her face. However, Aladdin hid near the bathhouse. He caught a glimpse of the princess's face when she lifted her veil as she walked in the door. She was so beautiful that Aladdin instantly fell in love with her.

Aladdin told his mother that he meant to ask the sultan for his daughter's hand in marriage. His mother laughed but Aladdin persuaded her to go to the sultan and present his request. She took the jewels from the trees in the cave with her, wrapped in a cloth.

For six days, Aladdin's mother went to sultan's hall, waiting for an audience. Finally, the sultan said to his vizier, 'I've seen that woman in the audience chamber for six days now, carrying something in that cloth. If she's here tomorrow, see what she wants.'

The next day, Aladdin's mother was summoned to the sultan. 'Tell me what you want, good woman,' said the sultan.

Aladdin's mother hesitated, so the sultan sent everyone away except for the vizier, promising he wouldn't take offence at what she was going to say. She told him of her son's love for his daughter and unfolded the jewels and presented them to the sultan.

The sultan was amazed by the priceless jewels. He turned to the vizier and said, 'See how much this man values my daughter? Surely I should allow them to marry.'

However, the vizier wanted his son to marry the princess. He convinced the sultan to wait three months before he gave his permission. The vizier hoped that he could make a richer gift and win the princess for his son. So the sultan agreed to Aladdin's proposal but told his mother that they must wait three months.

Aladdin waited. Two months went by, and then one day he discovered the townspeople rejoicing. 'Tonight the vizier's son is to marry the sultan's daughter!' they told him.

Aladdin fetched the lamp. He rubbed it and the genie appeared before him, saying, 'What is your will?'

'The sultan has broken his promise,' replied Aladdin. 'The princess marries the vizier's son. Bring them here tonight.'

'I obey, master,' said the genie.

Under the laws of the city, a couple were not married until they spent a night together. That night, the genie transported the princess and the vizier's son to Aladdin's house. 'Take this man and put him outside.' Aladdin said to the genie, 'Bring him in at daybreak.'

The genie took the vizier's son out, leaving the princess with Aladdin. 'Do not fear,' he said to her. 'You are promised as my wife and no harm shall come to you.'

The princess spent a miserable night, as she was too frightened to sleep. In the morning, the genie fetched in the cold, shivering bridegroom and transported them back to the palace.

When the sultan came to wish them good morning, the vizier's son hid and the princess looked miserable. She wouldn't speak to her father but told her mother how she had been carried to a strange house where the vizier's son had been sent away. Her mother told her that it must have been a dream.

But the same thing happened the following night. The next morning, the princess told the sultan what had happened. The vizier's son refused to marry the princess, saying he'd rather die than go through another night like that.

Aladdin sent his mother to remind the sultan of his promise, but the sultan was reluctant to grant his permission. He told Aladdin's mother, 'Your son may marry my daughter, but he must send me forty basins of gold filled with jewels, carried by forty slaves, who are lead by another forty slaves, all splendidly dressed.'

Aladdin's mother went home, thinking all was lost. But Aladdin summoned the genie of the lamp and soon eighty slaves arrived, forty of them carrying gold basins filled with jewels. They set out for the palace with Aladdin's mother. Everyone crowded to see them.

Aladdin's mother entered the palace and bowed to the sultan. The sultan said, 'Tell your son I wait for him with open arms.'

Aladdin called the genie. 'I want a scented bath, an embroidered robe, a fine horse and twenty slaves. I need six slaves to wait on my mother and ten thousand gold pieces in ten purses.' And it was done.

Aladdin mounted his horse and rode to the palace, followed by slaves throwing gold pieces to the cheering crowd. The sultan welcomed Aladdin and asked him to marry his daughter that day, but Aladdin said he had to build a palace for the princess first.

Aladdin said to the genie, 'Build a palace of finest marble set with precious stones. Put a large domed hall in the middle with walls of gold and silver. Put windows of diamonds and rubies in each wall. There must be stables, horses, grooms and slaves.'

The palace was finished the next day. Aladdin and his mother went to the sultan's palace. They were met by musicians and dancers. The princess was charmed by the handsome Aladdin. The princess told him that she was very happy to obey her father and marry him. They danced at the wedding feast until midnight and then returned to Aladdin's palace.

The next day, Aladdin invited the sultan to see the palace. The sultan was astounded, but the jealous vizier hinted that it must be the work of magic. However, Aladdin had won the heart of the sultan, who made Aladdin the captain of his armies. Over the next few years, Aladdin lived happily with the princess and won several battles for the sultan, but he remained courteous and modest.

However, far away, the evil magician remembered Aladdin. He was furious when he heard that Aladdin had escaped, married a princess and was living in great honour and wealth instead of perishing. This could have only happened with the lamp and so the magician set out to seize it for himself. He was determined to see Aladdin ruined.

When he arrived in the town, the magician discovered that Aladdin had gone hunting. The magician went to the market and bought a dozen new lamps. He put them in a basket and dressed as a peddler. He made his way towards Aladdin's palace, crying out, 'New lamps for old!' The townspeople laughed at this poor trade.

The princess was sitting in the garden when she heard the crowd laughing. She sent a slave to find out what the fuss was about. When she heard that a peddler was exchanging old lamps for brand new ones, she told the slave to take the old lamp from the shelf and exchange it. Now this was the magic lamp, which Aladdin could not take hunting with him.

Amidst the jeers of the crowd, the slave made the exchange. The magician ran out of the city gates. He waited until night and then rubbed the lamp. At his command, the genie carried the palace, the princess and the magician far away.

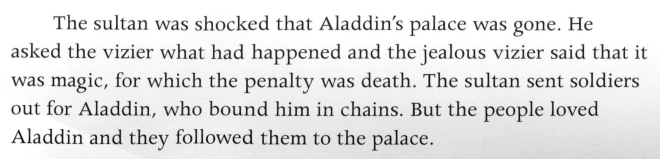

The sultan was shocked that Aladdin's palace was gone. He asked the vizier what had happened and the jealous vizier said that it was magic, for which the penalty was death. The sultan sent soldiers out for Aladdin, who bound him in chains. But the people loved Aladdin and they followed them to the palace.

The sultan ordered the executioner to cut off Aladdin's head, but the crowd forced their way in to rescue him. They were so threatening that the sultan ordered the executioner to stop. Aladdin begged to know what he had done. 'Where is my daughter?' demanded the sultan. 'Find her or you will lose your head!'

Aladdin begged the sultan to give him forty days to find her. If he couldn't, he promised to return and the sultan could do what he wished. The sultan agreed and Aladdin went to find the princess.

Aladdin wandered for several days. No one could tell him what happened to his palace. He came to a river and in despair decided to throw himself in. He knelt to pray, but as he did, he rubbed the magic ring, which he still wore. The genie of the ring appeared and asked him what his wish was. 'Bring my palace back!' said Aladdin.

'I do not have that power,' answered the genie of the ring. 'Only the genie of the lamp can do that.'

'Can you take me to my palace outside my wife's window?' asked Aladdin.

Aladdin found himself far away under the princess's window. When she saw Aladdin again, the princess was delighted and kissed him joyfully. 'Tell me, my love,' asked Aladdin, 'what happened to the old lamp that I left on the shelf?'

'It is all my fault!' exclaimed the princess. She told how she had exchanged the lamp. 'The magician has it,' she said. 'He wishes to marry me and says that my father beheaded you, but I refuse him.'

Aladdin went into a nearby town, bought a powder and snuck into the palace. 'Put on a beautiful dress and pretend you have forgotten me,' he told the princess. 'Invite him to eat with you and ask to try some wine. I will tell you what to do.'

The princess dressed in her finest clothes and received the magician. 'I have decided to mourn for Aladdin no more,' she said. 'Eat with me and let us try some of the wines of your country.'

The magician was dazzled by her beauty and smiles and ran to the wine cellar. Meanwhile, the princess put some of Aladdin's powder into the magician's cup. The magician returned, drank the wine from his cup and fell down dead. Aladdin quickly retrieved the lamp and asked the genie to set things right. How pleased the sultan was to see the palace returned and his daughter safe!

Aladdin thought he could live in peace, but it wasn't to be. The magician's brother was even more wicked and cunning and came to avenge him. He stole a holy woman's clothes and went to Aladdin's palace, his face hidden by a veil. A crowd gathered around him as he went, thinking he was a holy woman, and asked for a blessing.

The princess heard the crowd and told a servant to see what was going on. The servant said it was a holy woman who could cure people with her touch. The princess invited the false holy woman to the palace. The magician's brother looked around the palace and said it was very fine. 'However,' he said, 'it is lacking something.'

'What is that?' asked the princess.

'Hang an egg of the mystical bird, the roc, from the dome and it would be the wonder of the world,' answered the false holy woman.

After this, the princess thought of nothing but a roc's egg. She told Aladdin that her joy in the palace was ruined because it didn't have a roc's egg. 'If that is all, you shall soon be happy,' he replied.

Aladdin rubbed the lamp and commanded the genie to bring him a roc's egg. But the genie gave a shriek that shook the palace.

'Haven't I done enough for you?' demanded the genie. 'Now you want the egg of the fearsome roc! This request doesn't come from you, but from the evil magician's brother! He is here, disguised as a holy woman! He has requested this, hoping you would be killed by the roc. This man intends to murder you.'

Aladdin told the princess that his head ached and he wished the holy woman to cure him. But when the false holy woman came near, Aladdin seized his dagger and slew him. The princess was horrified, but Aladdin said, 'This is no holy woman! This is the magician's evil brother!' and he told her how she had been tricked.

After this, Aladdin and the princess lived a long and happy life. When the sultan died, Aladdin succeeded him as ruler and reigned with the princess for many happy years.

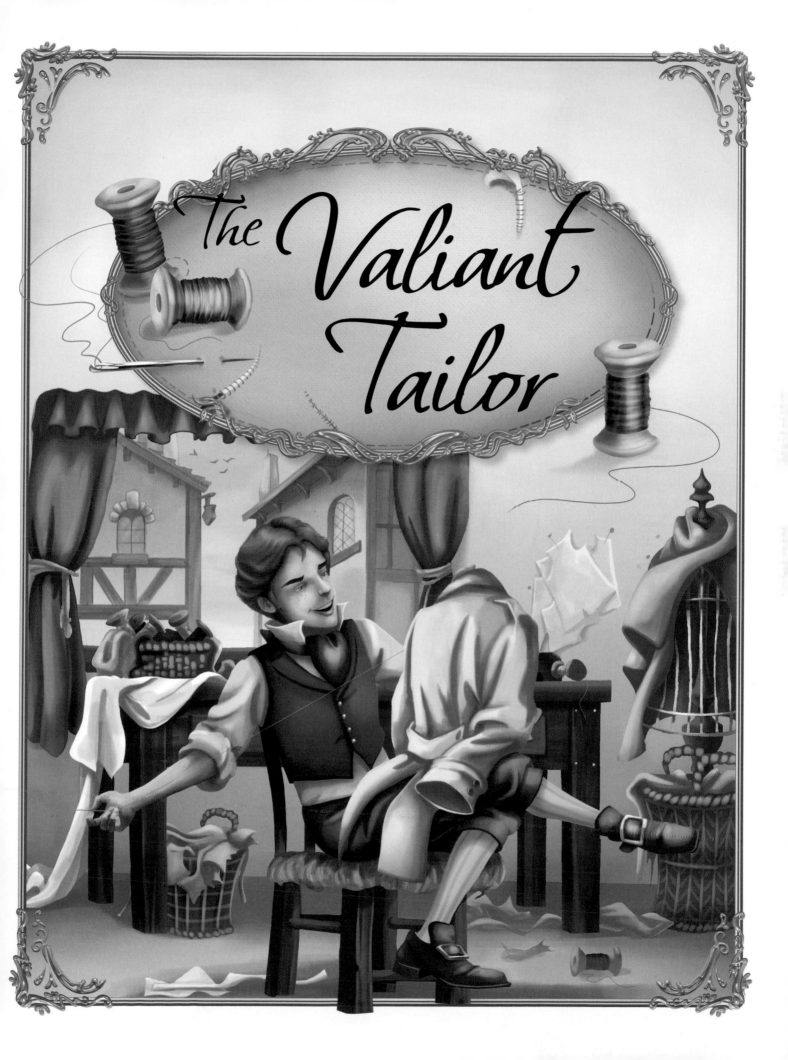

One summer's morning, a little tailor was sitting at his table near the window, working cheerfully away. As he worked, an old woman came down the street, shouting 'Good jams for sale! Good jams for sale, nice and cheap!'

This sounded like an excellent idea to the tailor, so he leaned out of the window and called out, 'Here, dear woman! I will buy some of your goods!'

The old woman climbed the steps to the window with her heavy basket. The tailor made her unpack all her pots, each of which he inspected closely. He lifted all the lids and sniffed each one. Finally, he said, 'This jam here seems to be quite good. Weigh me out four ounces please, dear woman.'

The woman had hoped to make a good sale, so she grumbled and complained as she weighed out the tiny amount, but the tailor was very pleased. He cut some bread and spread the jam on it, then laid it next to him while he continued working.

All the while, the smell of the sweet jam spread through the room. Soon some flies were attracted by the jam's lovely aroma and flew down to hover over the bread.

'Now then! Who invited you?' exclaimed the tailor, and he waved the uninvited flies away.

The flies, however, didn't seem to understand him, and returned in even larger numbers. Losing his patience, the tailor picked up a piece of leftover cloth from his table. He swatted away at the flies with the cloth, saying, 'Now you shall have it!'

When the tailor stopped swatting away, he counted the slain and found seven flies lying dead before him with their legs stretched out. 'This is indeed remarkable,' said the tailor, impressed at his own bravery. 'Why, the whole town should know of this!'

The tailor made himself a belt. He stitched on it, in large letters, 'Seven killed with one blow!' He put on his new belt and decided to go out into the world.

Before he went out, the tailor looked around the house to see what he could take with him. He found nothing but a hunk of soft cheese, which he put in his pocket. As he went out, he spied a bird caught in the thicket next to his door. He freed the bird and stowed it safely in his pocket with the cheese. Then he set out on his way.

The road the little tailor took led him up a mountain. When he reached the highest point, he saw a huge giant sitting there. The tailor walked up to him and said, 'Good day friend. I am on my way to try my luck in the world. Would you like to come with me?'

The giant looked at the tailor and screwed up his face. 'You little rascal! You miserable ragamuffin!' the giant said scornfully.

'Indeed?' said the little tailor, and he unbuttoned his coat and showed the giant his belt. The giant read, 'Seven killed with one blow!' and thought it meant men, not flies. He began to feel some respect for the tailor. But the giant still wanted to test the tailor, so he picked up a stone and squeezed it so hard that water come out of it.

'Can you do that?' asked the giant.

'Is that all?' asked the little tailor. 'A child could do that!' And he reached into his pocket and took out the cheese. He squeezed it until liquid ran out of it and asked, 'What do you think of that?'

The giant thought it was a stone in the tailor's hand and he didn't know what to say.

Then the giant picked up another stone and threw it so high that it nearly disappeared from sight. 'Can you do that?' asked the giant.

'That was a nice throw,' replied the little tailor, 'but the stone fell back to earth. I will throw one so high that it won't come down at all.' He felt in his pocket, took out the little bird and threw it into the air. The bird, happy that it was free, flew into the air and did not return.

'There is no doubt you can throw,' said the giant. 'But can you carry?' He took the tailor to a mighty oak tree that had fallen down and was lying on the ground. 'If you are strong enough, help me carry this tree out of the wood.'

'Gladly,' replied the tailor. 'You take the trunk on your shoulders and I will take the branches and leaves, as they are the most difficult to carry.'

The giant picked up the trunk on his shoulders, but the little tailor sat himself down in the branches. The giant, who could not look back with the trunk on his shoulders, carried the whole tree by himself. The tailor whistled as they went along.

Eventually, the giant cried out, 'I cannot carry it any further!' and dropped the tree. The tailor jumped off quickly and took hold of the branches as though he had been carrying it the whole time. 'You are such a big fellow, but you can't even carry a tree!' the tailor exclaimed.

They went on a little further and came to a cherry tree. The giant took hold of the top of thc tree and pulled it down towards him so the tailor could pick some of the fruit. But when the tailor took hold of the tree, the giant let go, and the tailor was tossed up into the air. When he dropped down again, the giant said, 'How is this? Don't you have enough strength to hold on to a little tree like this?'

'That was no lack of strength,' replied the tailor. 'I jumped over the tree because I heard some huntsmen shooting over in that thicket. See if you can jump it, if you dare.'

The giant tried to jump over the tree but he got stuck in the branches. After he got himself down, the giant said to the tailor, 'If you are such a brave fellow, come to my cave and spend the night with my fellow giants.'

The tailor agreed and followed the giant to the cave. There were other giants there, sitting around a fire and roasting a sheep. The giant showed him where to sleep. However, the bed was very big, so the tailor did not stay in it but crept into a corner to sleep. Around midnight he awoke and saw the giant take up an iron bar and beat the bed with it. The giant thought he had put an end to the tailor.

As the sun rose the next morning, the giants went into the forest. The little tailor had arisen earlier and gone for a walk in the woods, and when the giants saw him walking towards them unhurt and cheerful, they were terribly frightened and ran away in a great hurry.

The little tailor walked on, following his nose. He walked for a long time until he came to a royal palace. As he was very weary, the little tailor lay on the grass in the palace courtyard and fell asleep. As he slept, the people of the palace came by and looked at him curiously. They read 'Seven killed with one blow!' on his belt, and thought he must be a great warrior. Some of the noblemen went and told the king about the little tailor and said that if a war should ever break out, he would be a useful and worthy man who should be pressed to stay at any price.

This idea pleased the king and he sent one of his men to ask the tailor if he would serve in the king's army. The messenger waited by the tailor's side until he awoke and then made him the offer. 'Why, this is why I have come here!' exclaimed the tailor. 'I am ready to enter the king's service.'

The little tailor was honourably received into the army and a special house was set apart for him. However, the rest of the soldiers were not pleased with this and wished the tailor a thousand miles away. 'What can we do?' the asked each other. 'If we quarrel and he should strike us, then seven of us will fall at each blow.'

The soldiers went as a group to the king and begged him to dismiss them all. 'We did not expect to serve with a man who could kill seven with one blow,' they said.

The king did not want to lose all his faithful soldiers and began to wish that he had never set eyes on the tailor. But he didn't dare dismiss a man who could kill the king and all his people, and then place himself on the throne.

The king thought for a long time, then sent for the tailor. He told the tailor that as he was so great a warrior, he had a proposal for him.

'There are two giants in a wood in my kingdom,' the king said. 'They cause great trouble with their robbery, murder, ravaging and burning and no one can go near them without putting themselves in danger. If you can kill these two giants, you shall have my only daughter for your wife and half the kingdom as your reward. I shall send one hundred horsemen with you to assist.'

'That would be something for a man like me!' thought the tailor. 'I shall subdue these giants,' he told the king, 'but I will not need the help of one hundred horsemen. He who can kill seven at one blow need not fear two.'

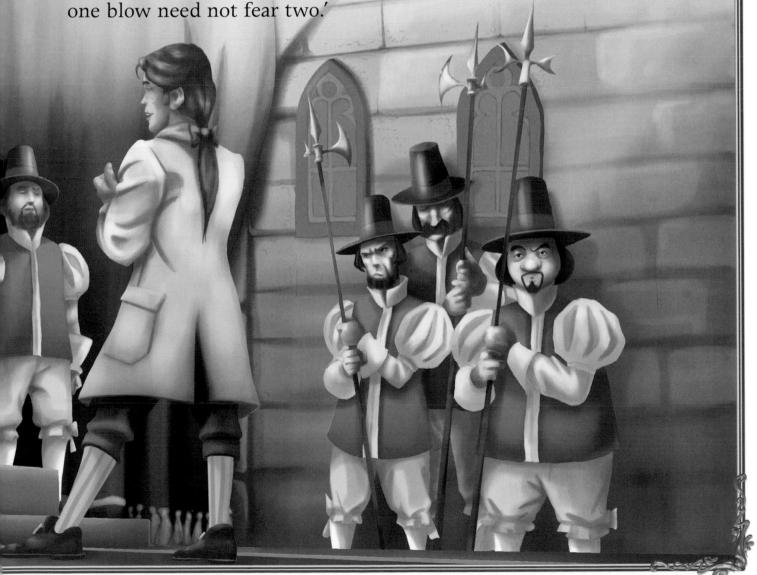

The tailor set out with the hundred horsemen. When he got to the edge of the wood, he told them to wait for him. He went into the wood and soon caught sight of the two giants asleep under a tree, snoring so hard that the branches shook.

The little tailor filled his pockets with stones and climbed the tree so that he was above the sleeping giants. Then he dropped one stone after the other on one giant's head. The giant awoke and pushed the other one. 'Why are you hitting me?' he asked angrily.

'It must be a dream,' said the other giant. 'I haven't touched you.'

Soon the two giants fell back to sleep. Again, the little tailor let more stones fall, this time on the head of the second giant. 'What is the meaning of this?' asked the second giant, waking up with a start. 'Why are you pelting me?'

'I have not thrown anything at you!' exclaimed the first giant, growling. The two giants argued for a while, but then grew quiet and fell back to sleep. The little tailor picked out the largest stone and threw it as hard as he could on to the head of the first giant.

'This is too much!' roared the first giant.

He jumped up and struck the second giant so hard that the whole tree shook. The second giant struck back with the same ferocity and the two giants got in such a rage that soon they were tearing up nearby trees and striking each other with all their might. At last, both giants fell down dead on the ground at the same time.

The little tailor jumped out of his tree, thinking it was lucky that neither of the giants tore up the tree he was in. He struck the giants a few times with his sword, then went back to the horsemen.

'The deed is done,' the tailor said. 'I have made an end to them both. It was a hard struggle and they uprooted many trees as they defended themselves, but I was the victor.'

The horsemen were amazed that the tailor was uninjured. Not believing his story, they rode into the forest to confirm it for themselves. They found the giants lying there, with uprooted trees all around them.

When he returned to the palace, the little tailor asked the king for his reward, but the king again tried to get rid of the hero. 'Before you can marry my daughter and take half my kingdom, you must perform another heroic act,' the king said. 'In another wood nearby there lives a unicorn that does great damage. You must catch him for me.'

'I fear one unicorn even less than I fear two giants!' replied the tailor. Taking some rope and an axe, he went alone into the wood. He soon saw the unicorn, who rushed towards the tailor as if it was going to run him through with its horn.

'Slowly, slowly. It can't be done quickly,' the tailor said to himself as the unicorn came charging towards him. He stood still until the unicorn was very close, then he nimbly sprung aside.

Now the clever tailor had been standing in front of a tree. The unicorn was running so fast that it could not stop in time and its horn became stuck in the trunk of the tree.

'Now I have caught you!' exclaimed the tailor. He placed the rope around the unicorn's neck and cut the trunk of the tree to free its horn. Then he led the beast away back to the king.

One night after the wedding, the king's
daughter heard the tailor talking in his sleep. 'Now boy,
make me that waistcoat and patch those breeches or I'll rap my ruler
over your shoulders!' he muttered as he lay dreaming.

The king's daughter realised what low origins the tailor had and
told her father, begging him to get rid of her husband, who was just
a tailor. The king told her to leave her bedroom door open and when
the tailor was asleep, the king's men would carry him off and send
him on a ship to the other side of the world. However, the king's
armour-bearer was friendly with the tailor and told him of the plot.

The tailor went to bed that night. When his wife thought he was asleep, she opened the door. The tailor then began to murmur, 'Now boy, make me that waistcoat and patch those breeches or I'll rap my ruler over your shoulders! I've slain seven at one blow, killed two giants, caught a unicorn and trapped a wild boar, so why would a nobleman like me fear those who are standing outside my door?'

When they heard this, the guards outside the door ran away in terror and none of them would dare attack him again.

The king's daughter again thought her husband was a nobleman. Eventually, she grew to love him dearly and the little tailor one day became the king of the whole kingdom.

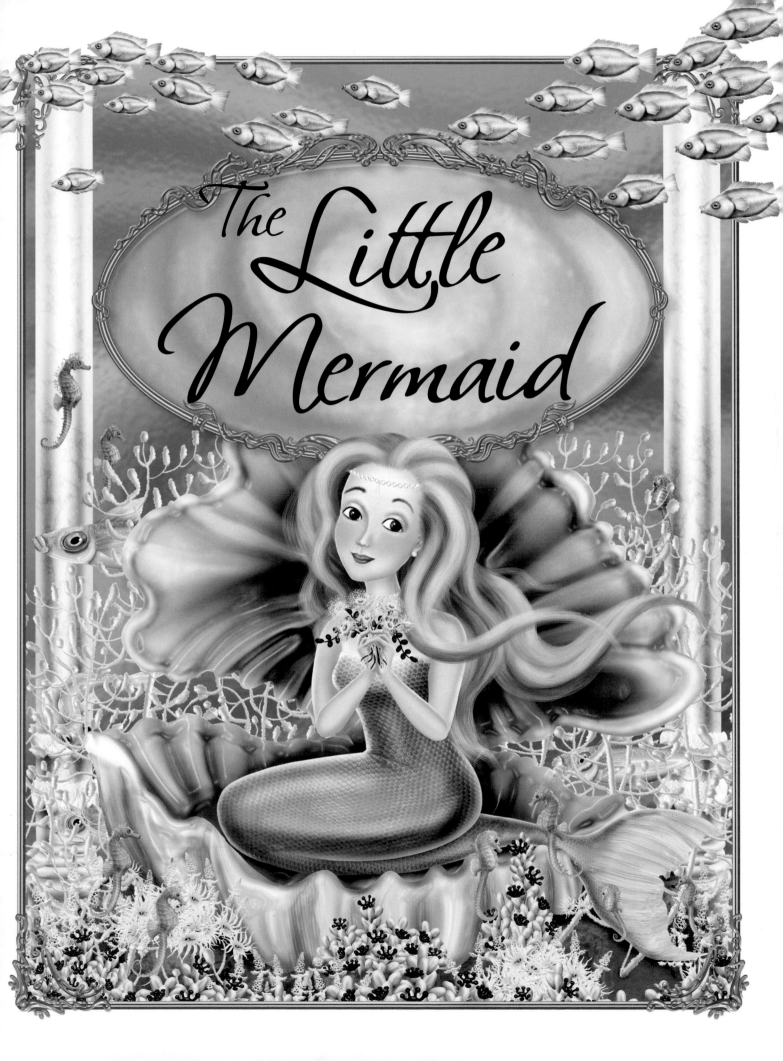

The Little Mermaid

Far out in the deep ocean, where the water is as blue as the sky and as clear as crystal, there lived the Sea King and his six daughters. He lived in a beautiful castle with walls made of coral, windows of amber and a roof of shells that opened and closed as the water flowed over them. Inside each shell was a glittering pearl. The castle was surrounded by a garden of lovely, colourful sea plants and flowers and was filled with fish both large and small.

The Sea King's wife had died many years ago, so his aging mother kept house for him. She was very old and wise and looked after the sea princesses. The Sea King's youngest daughter was the most beautiful of all, with skin as delicate as a rose petal and eyes as blue as the sea. Like all sea people, she had no legs and her body ended in a fish's tail.

All day the princesses played in the halls of the castle or swam in the gardens. Each of the princesses had their own little garden in the castle grounds where they could dig and plant whatever they wished. One had a flower bed in the shape of a whale, another made her's like a shell, but the youngest princess's garden was shaped like the sun, which could be seen in calm weather, shining down like a great flower. Her garden was full of red and yellow flowers, like the rays of the sun at dusk.

The only thing the youngest princess cared for more than her pretty flowers was a beautiful marble statue of a handsome boy. It was carved out of pure white stone and had fallen to the bottom of the sea from a wrecked ship. She loved to hear stories of the world above the sea. Her grandmother would tell her about ships, towns, people and animals.

'When you have turned fifteen,' said her grandmother, 'you will be allowed to swim to the surface, to sit on the rocks and see the great ships, the forests and the towns.'

When the oldest sister turned fifteen, she swam to the surface to see the world above. When she returned, she told her younger sisters such wonderful tales. She told them of the moonlight on a sandbank, the twinkling lights of a town, the sound of music and voices and the ringing of the church bells. The youngest sister longed to see these wonderful things.

As the years passed, each sister turned fifteen, and was allowed to swim to the surface to see the world above. The second sister returned with tales of the sunset, the sky golden with red clouds scurrying across it and a flock of wild swans flying towards the sun.

The third sister was the bravest and swam up a wide river. She saw green hills, palaces and castles, forests and birds. She came across little children playing in the river and wanted to join them, but a little black animal came and barked at her so she swam away. It was a dog but she had never seen one before.

The fourth sister stayed in the ocean, but saw great ships as large as castles, their sails white in the sun. She swam with leaping dolphins and saw huge whales spurting water into the air.

The fifth sister's birthday was in the winter. When she swam to the surface, she saw enormous icebergs, like huge, glittering pearls. She sat on an iceberg and watched a storm, with dark clouds, rolling thunder and blue lightning, darting across the sky.

Once they had turned fifteen, the older sisters could swim to the surface whenever they wished. But after a few months, they decided they preferred to stay at home. However, in the evenings, the five older sisters would swim together to the surface and sing to the sailors on the ships about the delights of the ocean, but the sailors never understood, thinking it was just the wind.

Finally, the youngest sister turned fifteen. She bade farewell to her grandmother and swam to the surface. The sun was just setting as she raised her head above the waves and the sky was crimson and gold. A large ship with three masts sat in the water. It was stuck where it sat, for there was no breeze at all, and the sailors were making merry on the deck. Music was playing and the ship was lit up with lanterns.

The mermaid swam closer to the ship and looked in the cabin windows. She saw a number of finely dressed people inside. Among them was a handsome young prince. It was his sixteenth birthday and everyone on the ship was celebrating.

The young prince went up to the deck, and suddenly hundreds of rockets rose into the air. The little mermaid was amazed as she watched the fireworks exploding and falling like stars. How handsome the prince looked as he watched the fireworks!

As time passed, the sailors put out the lanterns, but still the little mermaid watched. The sea started to become restless and the waves grew higher. As the wind rose, the sailors unfurled the sails and the ship continued on its way, but still the mermaid followed. Soon dark clouds were racing across the sky and a terrible storm approached. The waves rose higher and higher.

Soon, the main mast groaned and then snapped off. Some of the planks of the ship came loose. The little mermaid could see the sailors holding on with all their might, but she could not see the handsome prince.

Suddenly, a flash of lightning crashed across the sky and the little mermaid saw him struggling in the water. As the prince sank down, she swam to him. His eyes were closed and he was not moving. She helped him to the surface and kept his head above the water until morning.

As the sun rose and the storm passed, there was no sign of the ship. They were in sight of land and so the little mermaid took the prince in to shore. There were green hills in the distance and a large white building like a church or a convent. The little mermaid laid the unconscious prince in the sand.

Then a bell rang in the distance and some young girls came out of the white building. The little mermaid swam out to sea and hid behind some rocks. One young girl walked to the beach, where she found the prince lying in the sand. The prince came to and smiled at the girl, and then many people came to help him. But the prince had no smile for the little mermaid, as he did not know she had rescued him. The little mermaid was very unhappy as the prince was led away into the white building. She returned home to the Sea King's castle.

After this, the little mermaid was always quiet and sad. She often swam to the beach where she had left the prince, but she never saw him. Her only comfort was to sit in her garden, but she let the flowers grow wild and it became very dark and gloomy.

At last she asked her sisters and they showed her where the prince's palace was. The little mermaid spent many days and nights in the sea near the palace, watching him. She saw him sailing his boat or walking on the shore. As she watched, she also saw other people and heard fisherman talking. She grew more and more fond of humans. Finally, she went to her grandmother and asked, 'Do humans live forever?'

'No,' replied her grandmother. 'They must die, and they do not live as long as we do. But when we die, we become the foam on the surface of the ocean and have no immortal souls. Humans have a soul that lives forever, even after they die.'

'So I will die and never hear the music of the waves or see the red sun. Is there nothing I can do to gain an immortal soul?' asked the little mermaid.

'Only if a man were to love you so much that you meant everything to him and he promised to be true to you alone,' replied her grandmother. 'But this could never happen, for we cannot walk among them. Be happy and swim in the ocean.'

The little mermaid was not content. She decided to visit the Sea Witch. She travelled past foaming whirlpools and bubbling mud. The Sea Witch's house lay in the middle of a strange forest full of plants with slimy branches like worms. The witch's house was made of bones and was surrounded by fat water snakes.

'I know what you want,' the Sea Witch said when she saw the little mermaid. 'You are very silly. You will get what you wish, but it will bring you nothing but sadness. You want legs like a human so the prince will fall in love with you and give you an immortal soul.'

The little mermaid nodded. The Sea Witch laughed and said, 'I will make you a potion. Swim to the shore before sunrise and drink it. Your tail will be replaced by legs, but every step will feel like you are standing on sharp knives. You can never be a mermaid again nor return to your home and family. And if the prince does not love you and marries another, you will become the foam on the waves. If you can bear that, I will help you.'

'I can bear it,' said the little mermaid.

'I must be paid,' said the Sea Witch. 'You have the sweetest voice of all the creatures of the sea. You must give it to me.'

The little mermaid was sad but she agreed. The witch prepared the potion and took the little mermaid's voice. The little mermaid returned home, where everyone was asleep. She took a flower from each of her sisters' gardens to remember them, and then swam away for the last time. She swam to shore and drank the potion, then swooned. The next thing she knew, the sun was up and the handsome prince was standing before her.

She realised that instead of her fish tail, she had legs. The prince asked where she was from but she could not answer, as she had no voice. The prince took her back to his castle. Every step felt as though she was walking on needles, but she walked gracefully. They dressed her in robes of silk and she was the most beautiful woman in the palace, but she could not speak.

The prince was charmed by her beauty and said she should stay with him always. She accompanied him everywhere he went. As the days passed, she loved the prince more and more, and he loved her as he would love a child, but he never thought to marry her.

'You are dear to me,' the prince told her, 'but there is only one woman in the world I could love. I was shipwrecked and the waves cast me to shore near a church. A young woman found me there and saved my life. She serves the church still.'

'He doesn't know it was me who saved him,' thought the little mermaid. 'I was the one who carried him to shore and I saw the pretty maid he loves more than me. But he shan't marry her as she serves the church.'

It was decided by the king and queen that the prince should marry. The daughter of a nearby king was to be his wife, so the little mermaid went on a ship with the prince and his court to visit them.

'I must visit her,' said the prince to the little mermaid, 'but they cannot force me to love her or marry her.'

One night as the ship was sailing, the little mermaid sat on the deck looking at the waves. She thought she could see her father's castle in the waters below. Then her sisters came to the surface and waved to her. She beckoned to them, but a cabin boy came by and so they dived down.

The next morning, the ship sailed into the beautiful harbour of the king. There was a big parade waiting to meet them. The princess had not yet arrived, as she was being educated in a church to learn the royal virtues.

At last she arrived and the little mermaid had to admit she was the most beautiful woman she'd ever seen. She was fair, with laughing blue eyes that shone with truth and purity.

When he saw her, the prince let out a cry and exclaimed, 'It was you who saved me when I lay shipwrecked on the beach! Oh, I am too happy! All my dreams have come true.'

He took the princess in his arms. The little mermaid felt as though her heart was breaking. She knew that when he married, she would change into the foam of the waves by the next morning and would never have an immortal soul.

That night, the prince was married, but the little mermaid only thought of the death that was coming to her. She was dressed in beautiful silks and she danced more gracefully than she had ever danced before. Even though it hurt her tender feet, she did not feel it, because the pain in her heart was much greater. The prince took his bride to his ship where the celebrations continued into the night. Then the ship grew quiet as everyone fell asleep.

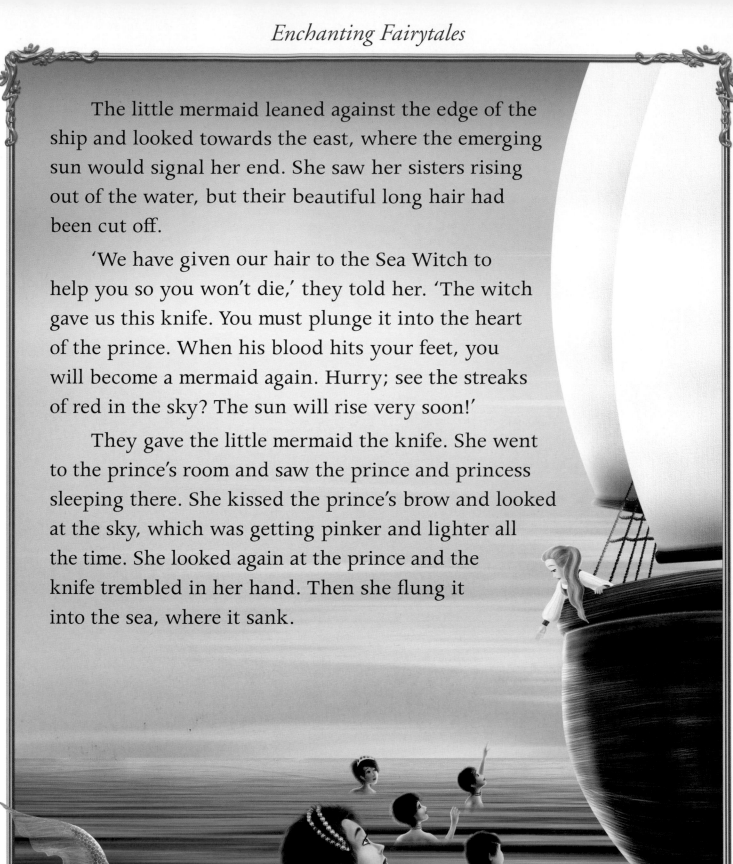

The little mermaid leaned against the edge of the ship and looked towards the east, where the emerging sun would signal her end. She saw her sisters rising out of the water, but their beautiful long hair had been cut off.

'We have given our hair to the Sea Witch to help you so you won't die,' they told her. 'The witch gave us this knife. You must plunge it into the heart of the prince. When his blood hits your feet, you will become a mermaid again. Hurry; see the streaks of red in the sky? The sun will rise very soon!'

They gave the little mermaid the knife. She went to the prince's room and saw the prince and princess sleeping there. She kissed the prince's brow and looked at the sky, which was getting pinker and lighter all the time. She looked again at the prince and the knife trembled in her hand. Then she flung it into the sea, where it sank.

The little mermaid threw herself into the sea as the sun rose and thought she felt herself dissolving into foam. Then she realised she was being drawn up into the air, surrounded by hundreds of transparent beautiful creatures. The little mermaid saw that her body had become just like theirs. 'Where am I?' she asked, and realised she had a voice; a voice that was like a song.

'You are with the daughters of the air,' the creatures answered. 'A mermaid can only gain an immortal soul if she wins the love of a human being. But a daughter of the air can gain one through her good deeds. After we have striven to do good for three hundred years, we gain an immortal soul. You, poor mermaid, have tried with your whole heart to do good. You have suffered and endured and so you have joined the daughters of the air.'

The little mermaid looked up to the sun and felt her eyes filling with tears of joy. She saw the people on the ship looking for her. Unseen, she kissed the foreheads of the bride and the prince and then rose into the sky with the daughters of the air.

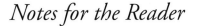

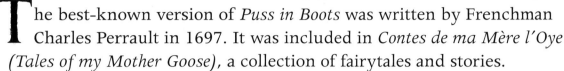

The best-known version of *Puss in Boots* was written by Frenchman Charles Perrault in 1697. It was included in *Contes de ma Mère l'Oye (Tales of my Mother Goose)*, a collection of fairytales and stories.

It is thought that Perrault adapted his story from the earliest known recorded version of the tale called *Fortunato Costantino*. This was written by an Italian, Giovanni Francesco Straparola, in the 1550s, who included it in his collection of stories, *The Facetious Nights of Straparola*. Another Italian, Giambattista Basile, included a version called *Caglioso* in the collection *Il Pentamerone* in the 1630s.

There are many variants of the *Puss in Boots* story that can be found in different cultures around the world. The cat is not always male in these stories: sometimes she is female. Animals other than cats are also used in the helper role, such as a fox or a gazelle. In some versions, the cat is actually a fairy in disguise or a woman who has been bewitched, who ends up marrying her master once the spell has been removed.

Another common variation has the cat testing its owner's gratitude by pretending to be dead or dangerously ill. The owner promises the cat a burial in a golden coffin when it dies. However, when the owner refuses to provide treatment for the sick cat or orders the supposedly dead cat's body be thrown on a dung heap or down a well, the cat either angrily takes its leave or reveals the humble origins of its owner. Perrault opted for a much happier ending for his cat, living out a life of leisure and amusement.

Aladdin

Aladdin was originally published in the collection *1001 Arabian Nights*, which was translated from Arabic into French by Antoine Galland. However, the story of *Aladdin* never appeared in the original Arabic manuscript but was actually added by Galland in 1710.

Galland claims to have heard the original version of *Aladdin* from a storyteller named Hanna Diab from the city of Aleppo in Syria, who was visiting Paris in 1705. Early Arabic manuscripts of *Aladdin* have been found, however one was written after Galland's translation and the other is a copy of a lost earlier version.

The original story of *Aladdin* is set in China, despite the fact that the customs, names and titles of the rulers are very definitely Arabic. The sorcerer is from the Maghreb, a region of North Africa that includes Morocco, Tunisia and Algeria. At one time, these two regions would have been at the ends of the known world, emphasising how far the sorcerer travels to find the lamp and how far away he transports the Princess.

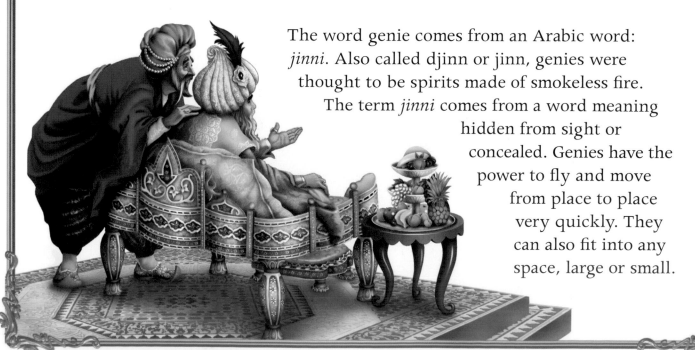

The word genie comes from an Arabic word: *jinni*. Also called djinn or jinn, genies were thought to be spirits made of smokeless fire. The term *jinni* comes from a word meaning hidden from sight or concealed. Genies have the power to fly and move from place to place very quickly. They can also fit into any space, large or small.

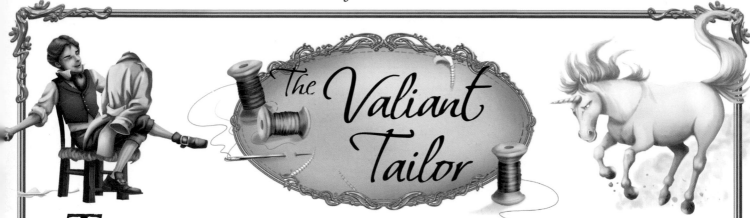

The Valiant Tailor

*T*he Valiant Tailor was published by the Brothers Grimm in the 1812 first edition of their collection of fairytales, *Kinder- und Hausmärchen (Children's and Household Tales)*. The story was revised in later editions into the version known today.

In their notes for the tale, the Grimm Brothers point out the many different versions of this tale that they found throughout Europe. The story's two parts can stand alone as individual tales, with the tailor's encounter with the giant the first and his three tasks the second.

The Grimms note that the first section is taken in part from an Austrian story where a tailor enters the service of a giant. The second part was taken from a collection of stories called *Wegkürzer* by Martinus Montanus. However, variations on the second part can

be found in stories from all over Europe, and as far afield as Persia. The profession of the tailor in these stories is sometimes changed to a cobbler.

The Grimm Brothers also note that the nature of the tailor's adventures with the giants vary in these stories. In one tale, the belt is replaced by a shield. The number of flies killed ranges from five to 500. The tasks the tailor performs also include killing a bear, defeating an army and overcoming two magicians. Whatever the variation, the tailor triumphs over his low origins through quick thinking, a sharp mind and his bravery, outwitting fearsome giants and royalty in the process.

The Little Mermaid

Written by Hans Christian Andersen in 1836, *The Little Mermaid* was first published in a collection called *Fairy Tales, Told for Children* in 1837. The story remains hugely popular, with adaptations created for theatre, ballet and film.

Hans Christian Andersen originally created the story with a much sadder ending, with the little mermaid dissolving away into foam. However, Andersen claimed that the working title of the story was 'The Daughter of Air' and that the ending where the little mermaid is transformed was intended from the start. This gives the little mermaid more control over her own destiny, instead of relying on the love of another.

Andersen later revised the ending to make it more moralistic. In the final version, whenever a child is good, a year is taken off the 300 years that the daughters of air must wait to receive their immortal soul. However, children's bad behaviour makes the daughters of air cry, which adds a day to their wait for every tear shed.

The story of *The Little Mermaid* is so popular that a small statute of the mermaid perched on a rock in Copenhagen harbour is one of Denmark's major tourist attractions.